Liam the Leprechaun Loves to Fart

By Humor Heals Us

Leprechauns are like small elves.
They always dress in green.
They're mischievous and magical,
And rarely ever **seen**.

They have a hidden pot of gold
At the end of the **rainbow**.
But if you try to follow them,
You won't have any luck, no!

Liam is a leprechaun
With a very special skill.
He does amazing magic farts.
The smell could almost kill.

His farts are loud and powerful,
And also very **smelly**.
So be careful not to get too close,
Or your knees will turn to jelly.

They'll grab their nose and hold their breath,
And quickly run away.
All attempts to find his gold
Will need to wait for another day.

His farts can shoot him up in the air.
And with one mighty **blow**,
Liam will **fly** across the sky
Holding on to a beautiful rainbow.

Leprechauns are sneaky.
They visit homes at night.
In their constant search for gold,
If you wake they'll flee in **fright**.

But Liam Leprechaun does not sneak well.
Although he tries his best
People wake up when he farts,
So finding gold's a **test**.

Now Liam guards all pots of gold
Because of his **brave** acts.
With his powerful secret weapon,
He fends off all attacks.

Liam now gets a percentage
Of all the gold they find
Because he's the **keeper** of the pots
And has to stay behind.

Leprechauns like all things green
In their food and drink.
But no matter what poor Liam eats,
His magic farts still stink.

Leprechauns are pranksters.
They're always playing tricks.
Liam sneaks up unannounced,
And farts loudly for kicks.

One day they held a meeting,
All the leaders of the Leprechaun Nation.
Liam released such a huge fart,
It caused **mass** evacuation.

So, if you see a leprechaun
With an "F" upon his pants,
It doesn't mean his name is Fred,
And don't let him near your plants.

Follow us on FB and IG @humorhealsus
To vote on new title names and freebies, visit
us at humorhealsus.com for more information.

@humorhealsus   @humorhealsus

Made in the USA
Middletown, DE
17 February 2021